STRING BASS
80SB

All for STRINGS

COMPREHENSIVE STRING METHOD•BOOK 3
by Gerald E. Anderson and Robert S. Frost

Dear String Student:

Welcome to **ALL FOR STRINGS, Book 3!**

By now, you have discovered that careful study and regular practice have brought you the joy and satisfaction of playing beautiful music.

The new playing technics and musical concepts found in **ALL FOR STRINGS, Book 3** will help you to continue your progress as a string player and musician.

We hope that **ALL FOR STRINGS, Book 3** will help make the road to your musical goals more enjoyable.

Best wishes!

Gerald E. Anderson
Robert S. Frost

ALL FOR STRINGS, Book 3 is published for the following instruments:
Violin   Viola   Cello   String Bass

Piano Accompaniment
    A separate book containing 89 piano accompaniments is recommended to students for home use, private instruction and ensemble practice.

ISBN 0-8497-3307-3

© **1991 Neil A. Kjos Music Company**, 4382 Jutland Drive, San Diego, California.
International copyright secured. All rights reserved. Printed in the U.S.A.
WARNING! The contents of this publication are protected by copyright law. To copy or reproduce them by any method is an infringement of the copyright law. Anyone who reproduces copyrighted matter is subject to substantial penalties and assessments for each infringement.

kjos NEIL A. KJOS MUSIC COMPANY • SAN DIEGO, CALIFORNIA

TUNING

1. TUNE YOUR INSTRUMENT

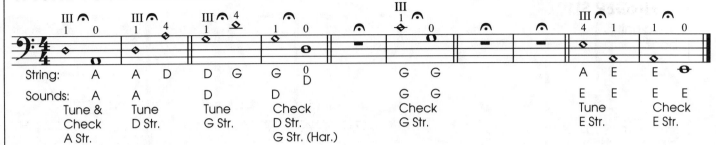

| String: | A | A | D | D | G | G | | G | G | | A | E | E |
| Sounds: | A | A | D | D | G | G | | G | G | | E | E | E | E |

Tune & Check A Str. | Tune D Str. | Tune G Str. | Check D Str. G Str. (Har.) | Check G Str. | Tune E Str. | Check E Str.

2. TUNING UNISONS

THEORY GAME

3. TUNING CHORDS (Root position)

★ What does "simile" mean? _____

4. TUNING CHORDS (Inversions)

5. TUNING CHORD PROGRESSIONS

6. A MIGHTY FORTRESS

Luther

VIBRATO

DEVELOP FINGER STRENGTH

7. FINGER SLIDES

Use a unit (forearm/wrist/hand) motion. Place only the finger needed and slide the unit (forearm/wrist/hand) back and forth as needed for each section. All other fingers should be off the string and relaxed. Keep 3rd finger next to the 4th finger for strength.

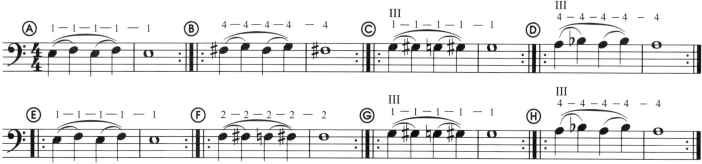

★ Be sure you have a good left hand position.

DEVELOP CORRECT VIBRATO MOTION

8. MATCHBOX SHAKE

    a. Tape a matchbox shut (with something inside). Without your instrument, hold your left hand/arm in playing position with the matchbox between your thumb, and 1st and 2nd fingers.
    b. Shake the matchbox up and down. Hold the matchbox as relaxed as possible (don't squeeze it). This is the basic vibrato motion.

9. POLISHING THE STRING

With your instrument only (no bow), play Exercises 7A through 7H using the rhythms below in both of the following positions:
    a. Place your 2nd finger lightly on the string. Move the unit (forearm/wrist/hand) including the 2nd finger and thumb back and forth with the vibrato motion. Slide your 2nd finger lightly on the string as if polishing the string. Do this with each finger. See diagram 1.
    b. Place your thumb in one place (regular playing position) against the neck. Place your 2nd finger lightly on the string and move the unit back and forth with a vibrato motion sliding your 2nd finger as you did in the previous exercise. Do not slide the thumb. See diagram 2.

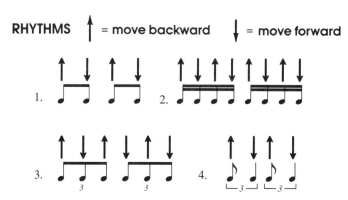 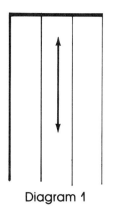 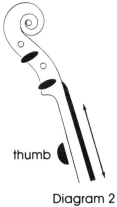

Diagram 1   Diagram 2

PLAY WITH VIBRATO

10. TETRACHORD SCALES

Play these tetrachord scales with a smooth and relaxed vibrato on each note.
Rest when your forearm, wrist, or hand gets tired.

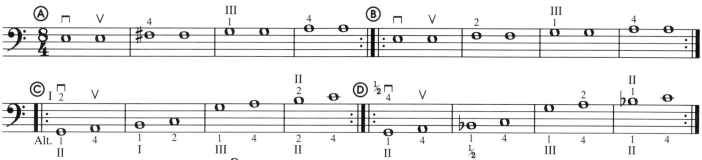

★ How many beats in a measure does $\frac{8}{4}$ time have? _____

11. C MAJOR

★ Apply the following bowings to lines 11 and 12. Also apply these bowings to lines 15, 16, 19, and 20.

12. C MAJOR REVIEW

Wohlfahrt Op. 45, no. 2

13. WELCOME TO ALL

Schubert-Round

Moderato

mf

★ Begin your pick-up note in the middle of the bow.

14. "NEW WORLD" SYMPHONY—THEME

Dvořák

Largo*

p

mf

Fine

D. C. al Fine

★ Play this piece using vibrato.
* Refer to page 18 for the tempo/dynamic glossary.

15. F MAJOR

★ Apply the following bowings to lines 15 and 16. Also apply these bowings to lines 11, 12, 19, and 20.

a.   b.   c.   d.

16. F MAJOR REVIEW

Wohlfahrt Op. 54, no. 1

17. THE BRITISH GRENADIERS

Schumann

Allegro moderato*

f   *mf*

f

f   *rit.*

* Refer to page 18 for the tempo/dynamic glossary.

18. THREE PIRATES

English Sea Chantey

Allegro

mf   *f*

dim.   *f*

19. D MAJOR

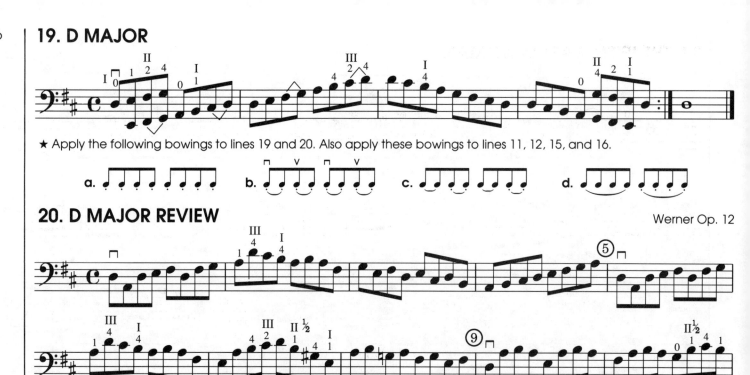

★ Apply the following bowings to lines 19 and 20. Also apply these bowings to lines 11, 12, 15, and 16.

a.　b.　c.　d.

20. D MAJOR REVIEW

Werner Op. 12

THEORY
GAME

21. ALL THROUGH THE NIGHT

Andante

Welsh Folk Song

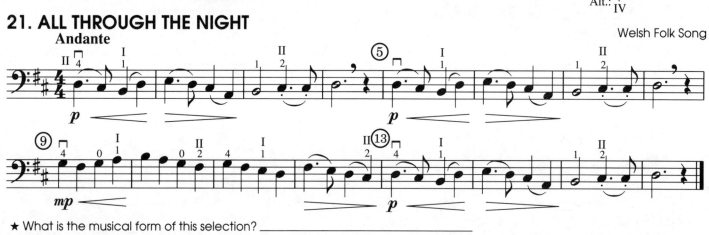

★ What is the musical form of this selection? _____

22. A CAPITAL SHIP

Vivace*

American Folk Song

* Refer to page 18 for the tempo/dynamic glossary.

23. THE IRISH WASHERWOMAN

Traditional

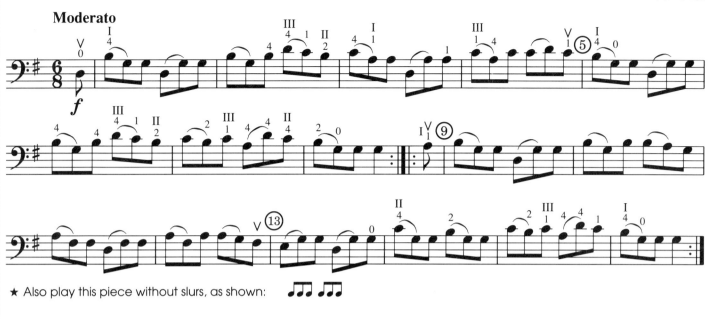

★ Also play this piece without slurs, as shown:

24. JIG

Irish Folk Song

★ Observe accents and staccato marks in lines 24 and 25.

25. MAZURKA

Wohlfahrt Op. 38, no. 62

NEW IDEA

DOTTED EIGHTH AND SIXTEENTH NOTES

$\frac{3}{4} + \frac{1}{4} = 1$ beat

$\frac{1}{4} + \frac{3}{4} = 1$ beat

Counting	1 e & a	2 e & a
Alternate Counting		

THEORY GAME

26. RHYTHM TRAINER

★ 1. Write in the counting. 2. Clap and count each line. 3. Play arco or pizzicato.
4. Practice each rhythm/bowing on the descending scale.

27. TECHNIC TRAINER

THEORY GAME

28. BATTLE HYMN OF THE REPUBLIC

Steffe

Moderato

mp

cresc.

f

rit.

★ Begin your pick-up note in the middle of the bow.   What does "*rit.*" mean? _____

29. THE MARRIAGE OF FIGARO—ARIA

Mozart

30. TECHNIC TRAINER

★ Play this exercise with the following bowings:

a. b. c. d.

31. LA DONNA E MOBILE

Verdi

32. RHYTHM TEASER

★ 1. Write in the counting. 2. Clap and count. 3. Play arco or pizzicato.

33. COLONIAL HYMN

Billings-Round

★ Play this piece using vibrato.
* Refer to page 18 for the tempo/dynamic glossary.

NEW IDEA

TIME SIGNATURE $\frac{3}{8}$ = 3 beats in each measure

Counting	1 &	2 &	3 &	1 &	2 &	3 &
Alternate Counting						

DOTTED EIGHTH AND SIXTEENTH NOTES

$1\frac{1}{2} + \frac{1}{2} + 1 = 3$ beats

THEORY GAME

34. RHYTHM TRAINER

★ 1. Write in the counting. 2. Clap and count each line. 3. Play arco or pizzicato.
   4. Practice each bowing/rhythm on the descending scale.

35. RHYTHMIC WALTZ

Wohlfahrt Op. 38, no. 66

Moderato

36. RHYTHM TEASER

★ 1. Write in the counting. 2. Clap and count. 3. Play arco or pizzicato.

37. SCHEHERAZADE

Rimsky-Korsakov

Allegro moderato

★ Use smooth bow changes.

38. TECHNIC TRAINER

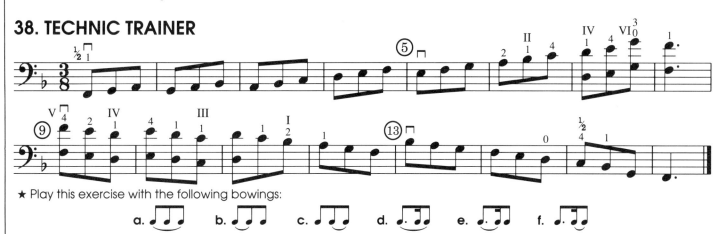

★ Play this exercise with the following bowings:

a.   b.   c.   d.   e.   f.

39. GREENSLEEVES

Old English Air

Moderato

40. SANTA LUCIA

Neapolitan Boat Song

Andante

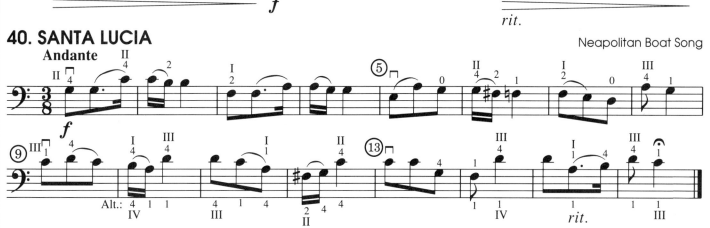

NEW IDEA

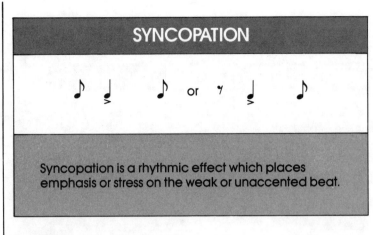

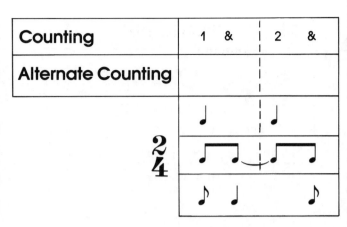

Counting	1	&	2	&
Alternate Counting				

SYNCOPATION

♪ ♩ ♪ or ⅂ ♩ ♪

Syncopation is a rhythmic effect which places emphasis or stress on the weak or unaccented beat.

THEORY GAME

41. RHYTHM TRAINER

★ 1. Write in the counting. 2. Clap and count each line. 3. Play arco or pizzicato.
   4. Practice each rhythm/bowing on the descending scale.

42. THE RIDDLE

Kentucky Folk Tune

Moderato

mf

rit.

43. POLKA

Slovakian Folk Song

Presto*

Alt.: IV

f

* Refer to page 18 for the tempo/dynamic glossary.

44. GO DOWN MOSES

Spiritual

Andante

★ Play this piece using vibrato.

45. RHYTHM TEASER

★ 1. Write in the counting. 2. Clap and count. 3. Play arco or pizzicato.

46. CARRY ME BACK TO OLD VIRGINNY

Bland

Moderato

★ Play this piece in the middle of the bow. Save bow on the ♩.   How many measures use syncopation? _____

47. DIXIE

Emmett

Allegro

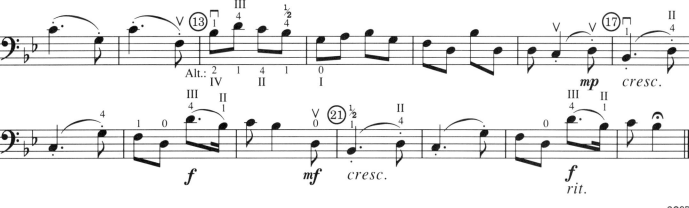

NEW IDEA

KEY SIGNATURE	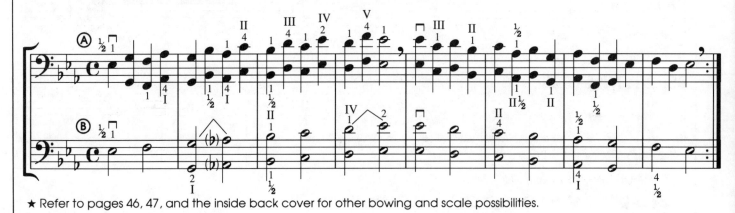	This is the key signature for E♭ Major. When you see this key signature, play all the B's as B♭, all the E's as E♭, and all the A's as A♭.

48. E♭ MAJOR SCALE AND BROKEN THIRDS

★ Refer to pages 46, 47, and the inside back cover for other bowing and scale possibilities.

49. E♭ MAJOR TRAINER

★ Play this exercise with the following bowings:

a.   b.   c.   d.

50. CRUSADER'S HYMN

German Air

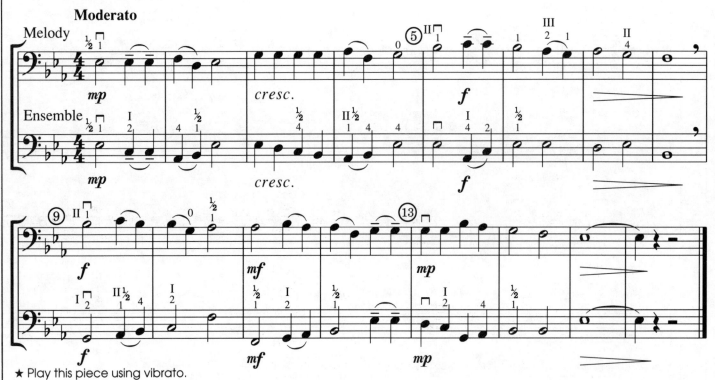

★ Play this piece using vibrato.

51. AUSTRIAN HYMN

Haydn

52. LAZY SAMMY

Hebrew-Round

53. MY OLD KENTUCKY HOME

Foster

★ Begin your pick-up note close to the frog of the bow.
* Refer to page 18 for the tempo/dynamic glossary.

54. WOODEN SHOE DANCE

Belgian Folk Song

★ *2x rit.* tells you to ritard. the second time through the piece.

NEW IDEA

KEY SIGNATURE	$\begin{array}{c}\text{\textcolor{white}{9:}}\\ \flat\flat\flat\end{array}$	This is the key signature for c minor. It is the same key signature as E♭ Major because c minor is the relative minor key.

55. C MINOR SCALES AND ARPEGGIOS

★ Refer to pages 46, 47, and the inside back cover for other bowing and scale possibilities.

56. C MINOR TRAINER

★ Play this exercise with the following bowings:

a.   b.   c.   d.

57. RISE UP O FLAME

Praetorius-Round

Moderato

58. FARANDOLE

Bizet

Allegro

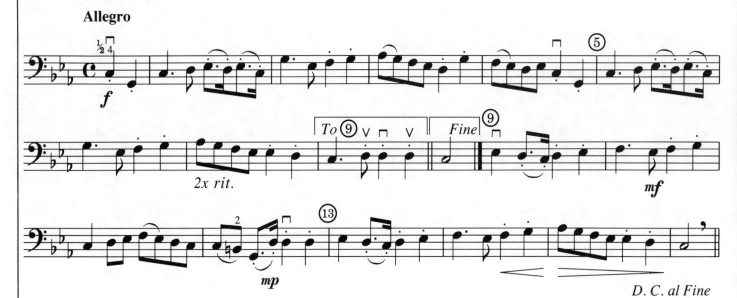

D. C. al Fine

| KEY SIGNATURE | | This is the key signature for E Major. When you see this key signature, play all the F's as F♯, all the C's as C♯, all the G's as G♯, and all the D's as D♯. |

59. E MAJOR SCALE AND BROKEN THIRDS

★ Refer to pages 46, 47, and the inside back cover for other bowing and scale possibilities.

60. E MAJOR TRAINER

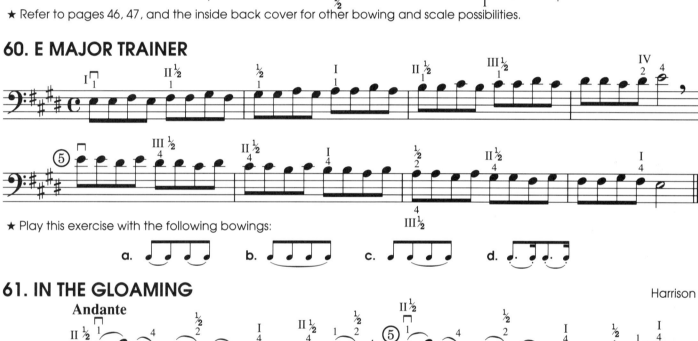

★ Play this exercise with the following bowings:

a.   b.   c.   d.

61. IN THE GLOAMING

Harrison

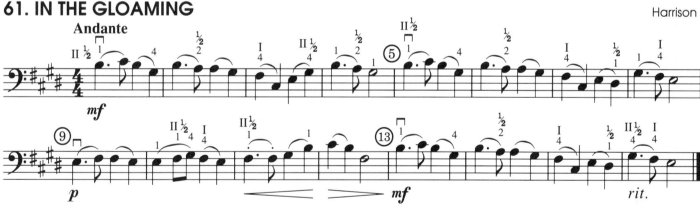

62. LOVELY MONTH OF MAY

Schubert-Round

NEW IDEA

SFORZANDO	$\dot{}$ sfz	Sforzando is a strong accent on a particular note or chord.

63. THE BARTERED BRIDE

Smetana

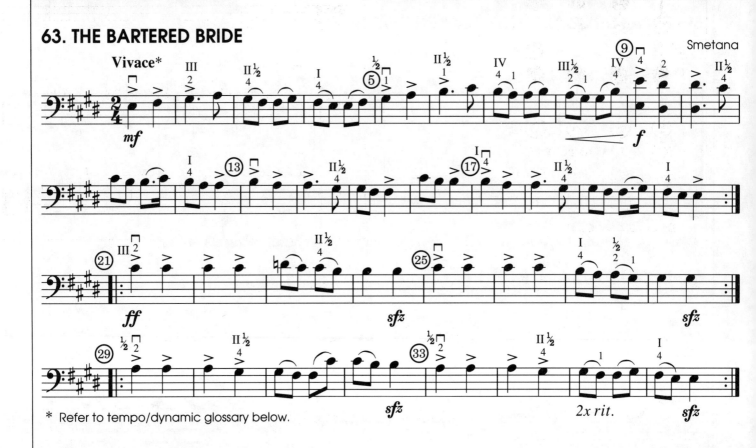

* Refer to tempo/dynamic glossary below.

NEW IDEA

TEMPOS	The Italian terms listed below represent the most common tempo and dynamic markings used in classical music.	DYNAMICS

Presto	very fast	*ff*	**Fortissimo**	very loud
Vivace	brisk and animated	*f*	**Forte**	loud
Allegro	quick and lively	*mf*	**Mezzo forte**	moderately loud
Moderato	moderate speed	*mp*	**Mezzo piano**	moderately soft
Andante	moderately slow	*p*	**Piano**	soft
Lento	slow, between Adagio and Andante	*pp*	**Pianissimo**	very soft
Adagio	slow and leisurely, not as slow as Largo	*cresc.*	**Crescendo**	increasing in loudness
Largo	very slow and broad			
a tempo	in the original speed	*dim.*	**Diminuendo**	diminishing in loudness
rit.	Ritard. gradually slow the speed			

DYNAMIC CHART

pp　　*p*　　*mp*　　*mf*　　*f*　　*ff*　　*f*　　*mf*　　*mp*　　*p*　　*pp*

NEW IDEA

NEW NOTES

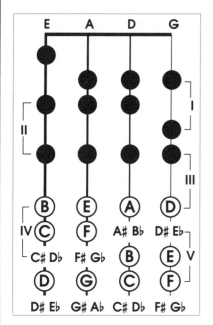

64. THIRD POSITION TRAINER FOR VIOLINS AND VIOLAS

65. C MAJOR SCALE, BROKEN THIRDS AND ARPEGGIOS

66. MARINES' HYMN

Offenbach

67. TECHNIC TRAINER

★ Play this exercise with the following bowings:

a.   b.   c.   d.

68. ANNIE LAURIE

Scottish Folk Song

Andante

★ Play this piece using vibrato.

69. G MAJOR SCALE, BROKEN THIRDS AND ARPEGGIOS

70. RONDEAU

Mouret

Moderato

THEORY GAME

71. THE MINSTREL BOY

Irish Folk Song

★ How many times do you shift into II position?_____ III position?_____ ½ pos.?_____

72. TECHNIC TRAINER

73. D MAJOR SCALE, BROKEN THIRDS AND ARPEGGIOS

74. JOY TO THE WORLD

Handel

75. TECHNIC TRAINER

★ Work for smooth string crossings.

76. BOHEMIAN FOLK SONG

Traditional

Allegro

77. F MAJOR SCALE, BROKEN THIRDS AND ARPEGGIOS

78. BARBARA ALLEN

English Folk Song

Moderato

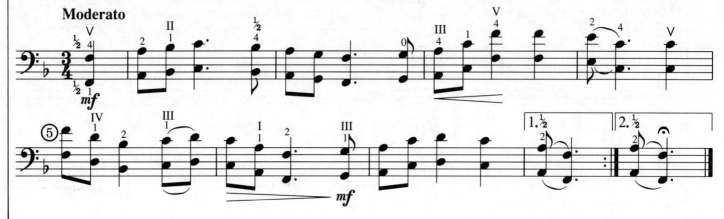

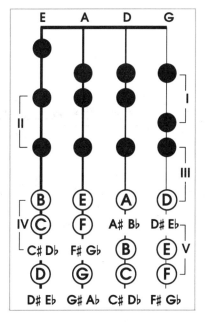

79. THIRD POSITION TRAINER FOR CELLOS

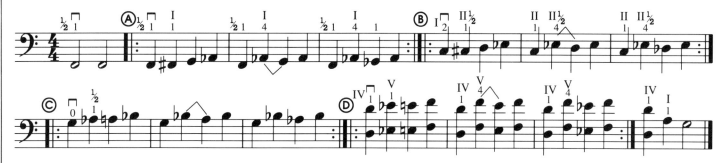

80. ORIGINAL FOLK DANCE

Anderson

Allegro moderato

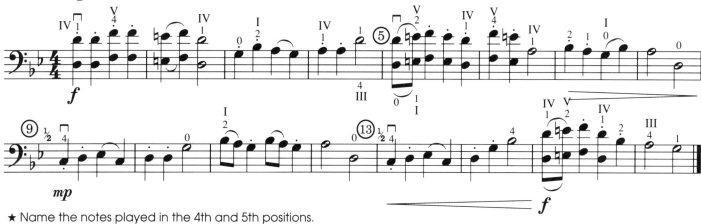

★ Name the notes played in the 4th and 5th positions.

81. ETUDE FOR CELLO

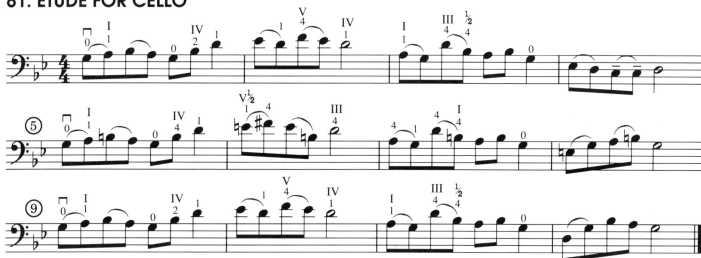

★ What is the musical form of this selection? _____

THEORY GAME

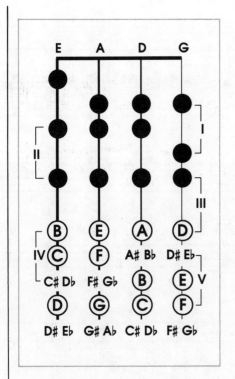

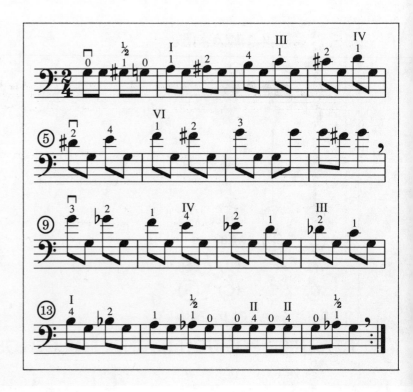

82. FOURTH POSITION TRAINER FOR CELLOS

83. MELODIC ETUDE IN A MINOR

Déak Vol. 1, no. 49

Fine

D. C. al Fine

FROM: MODERN METHOD FOR THE VIOLONCELLO – Vol. I
© 1929 Elkan-Vogel, Inc.
Reprinted By Permission Of The Publisher

★ This is the harmony part. Listen to the melody played by the violins, violas, and cellos.

THEORY
GAME

84. LAMENT

Anderson

Lento

Fine

★ What does "Lento" mean? _____

D. C. al Fine

85. TECHNIC TRAINER

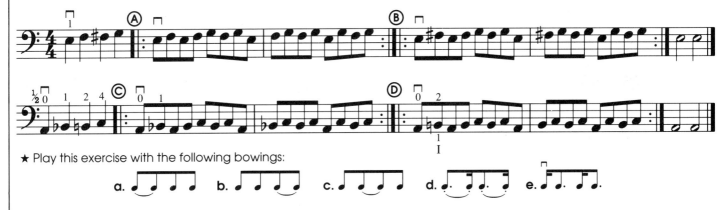

★ Play this exercise with the following bowings:

a. b. c. d. e.

THEORY
GAME

86. ANDANTINO

Werner Op. 12, no. 12a

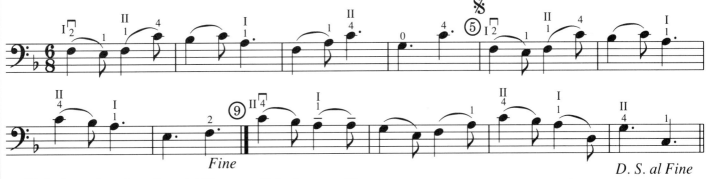

Fine

D. S. al Fine

★ Circle the notes where Type I shifts occur. Refer to page 27.

87. MELODIC ETUDE IN F MAJOR

Kummer

THEORY
GAME

88. BARCAROLLE

Offenbach

Moderato

rit.

D. C. al Fine

★ Play this piece using vibrato. Write in your own dynamics for this piece. Be sure to use crescendos and diminuendos.

80SB

NEW IDEA

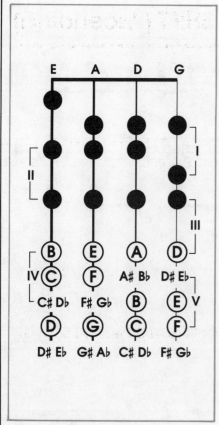

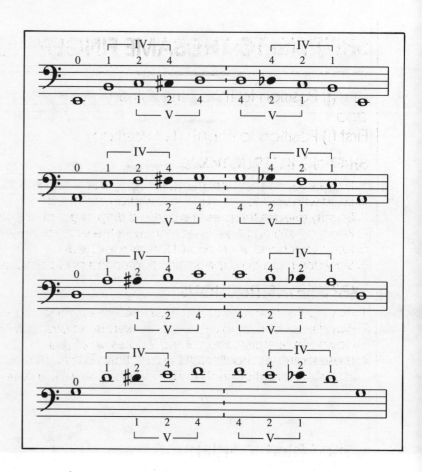

89. E MAJOR SCALE

90. THE OLD WOMAN AND THE PEDDLER

English Folk Song

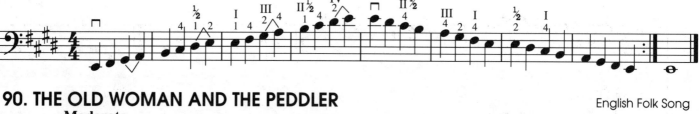

Moderato

91. F MAJOR SCALE

92. ETUDE FOR BASS

SHIFTING TO THE SAME FINGER – CLASS 1 SHIFT (Ascending)

First (I) Position to Third (III) Position
and
First (I) Position to Fourth (IV) Position

SHIFTING INSTRUCTIONS

1. Move your hand, thumb, fingers and forearm together.
2. Lead with your forearm in the direction of the shift.
3. Slightly release the pressure of the sliding finger during the shift.
4. Keep the sliding finger in contact with the string during the shift.
5. Keep your hand, thumb, and forearm relaxed.
6. Slow down the bow speed and lighten the bow pressure during the shift.

EXERCISE INSTRUCTIONS

1. Play the first measure of each exercise to establish intonation.
2. Play the second measure of each exercise to practice the shift.
3. Play each exercise also slurring 2 notes: ♩ ♩ ♩ ♩
4. These exercises should NOT be practiced all at one time. Select and practice a few exercises each day.
   Especially practice shifts encountered in your repertoire.

I. FIRST FINGER SHIFTS

II. SECOND FINGER SHIFTS

III. FOURTH FINGER SHIFTS

SHIFTING TO THE SAME FINGER – CLASS 1 SHIFT (Ascending)

NEW IDEA

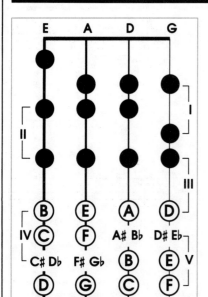

First (I) Position to Third (III) Position
and
First (I) Position to Fourth (IV) Position

SHIFTING INSTRUCTIONS

1. Move your hand, thumb, fingers and forearm together.
2. Lead with your forearm in the direction of the shift.
3. Slightly release the pressure of the sliding finger during the shift.
4. Keep the sliding finger in contact with the string during the shift.
5. Keep your hand, thumb and forearm relaxed.
6. Slow down the bow speed and lighten the bow pressure during the shift.

93. SHIFTING TRAINER

94. MARINES' HYMN

Offenbach

Allegro

★ This is the harmony part. Listen to the melody played by the violins and violas.

95. NIFTY SHIFTER

Anderson

★ Keep the sliding finger in contact with the string during the shift.

96. SHIFTING TRAINER

97. POLLY WOLLY DOODLE

American Folk Song

★ Play this piece with your best tone at all dynamic levels. What does "Presto" mean? _____

98. SHIFTING ETUDE NO. 1

Wohlfahrt Op. 74, no. 36

★ Keep the sliding finger in contact with the string during the shift.

99. AIR

Frost

Moderato

100. SHIFTING TRAINER

101. RUSSIAN FOLK SONG

Traditional

Allegro moderato

102. SHIFTING ETUDE NO. 2

Wohlfahrt Op. 45, no. 39

★ Keep the sliding finger in contact with the string during the shift.

103. CHORALE PRELUDE

Bach

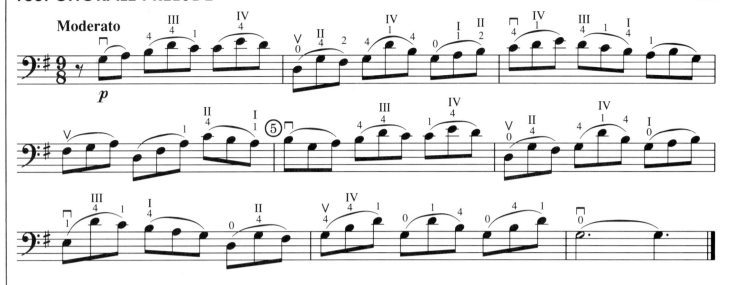

104. SHIFTING TRAINER

105. ALL FINGERS SHIFT

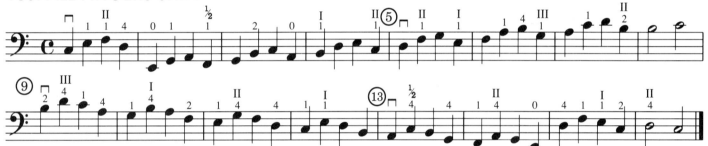

106. SONGS MY MOTHER TAUGHT ME

Dvořák

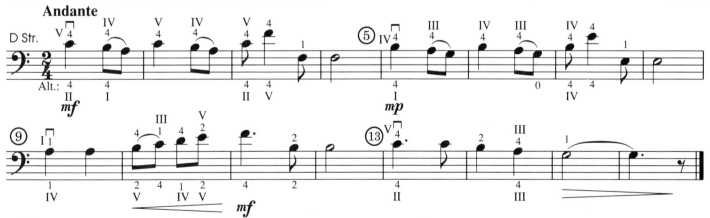

★ How many measures use syncopation? _____

107. ONE BY ONE

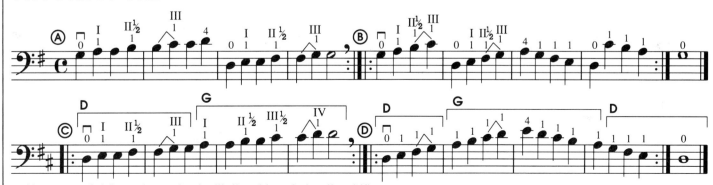

★ Keep your 1st finger in contact with the string during the shift.

SHIFTING TO A DIFFERENT FINGER – CLASS 2 SHIFT (Ascending)

Low Numbered Finger to a High Numbered Finger
First (I) Position to Third (III), Fourth (IV), and Fifth (V) Positions

SHIFTING INSTRUCTIONS

1. Shift up or down with the finger last used in the old position. This finger becomes the shifting guide finger.
2. Place the new finger immediately upon reaching the new position.
3. Move your fingers, hand, and forearm in a relaxed motion during the shift.

EXERCISE INSTRUCTIONS

1. These exercises should NOT be practiced all at one time. Select and practice a few exercises each day.
   Especially practice the shifts encountered in your repertoire.

I. G STRING

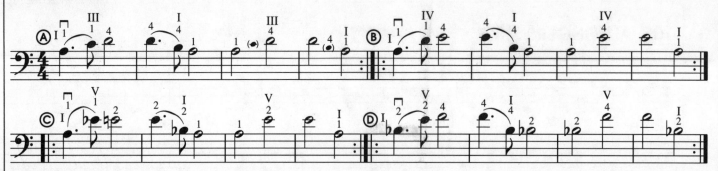

II. D STRING

III. A STRING

IV. E STRING

SHIFTING TO A DIFFERENT FINGER – CLASS 2 SHIFT (Ascending)

Low Numbered Finger to a High Numbered Finger
First (I) Position to Third (III), Fourth (IV), and Fifth (V) Positions

SHIFTING INSTRUCTIONS

1. Shift up or down with the finger last used in the old position. This finger becomes the shifting guide finger.
2. Place the new finger immediately upon reaching the new position.
3. Move your fingers, hand, and forearm in a relaxed motion during the shift.

108. SHIFTING TRAINER NO. 1

★ The descending shift is to the same finger.

109. SHIFTING TRAINER NO. 2

★ The descending shift is to a different finger.

110. SHIFTING ETUDE

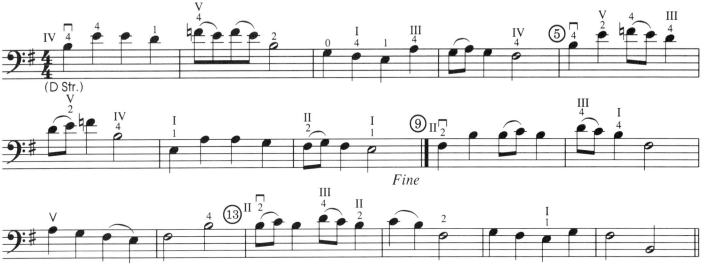

Fine

★ Shift to the new position using the guide finger.

D. C. al Fine

111. THE LION TAMER

Frost

Allegro moderato

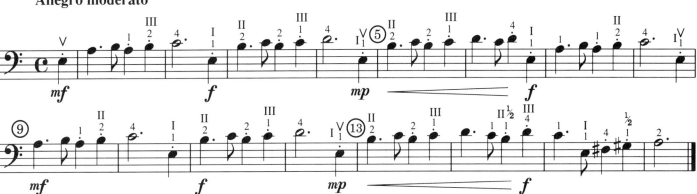

80SB

112. TO A WILD ROSE
MacDowell

★ Play this piece using vibrato.

113. APRIL
Brahms

★ Play with your best tone.

114. MELODY*
Rubinstein

Fine

D. C. al Fine

* This song is originally known as "Melody in F."

115. SHIFTING SERENADE
Anderson

Fine

★ Shift to the new position using the guide finger.

D. C. al Fine

SHIFTING TO A DIFFERENT FINGER – CLASS 3 SHIFT (Ascending)

High Numbered Finger to a Low Numbered Finger
First (I) Position to Third (III), Fourth (IV), and Fifth (V) Positions

SHIFTING INSTRUCTIONS

METHOD I
1. Shift up with the finger to be used in the new position. This finger becomes the shifting guide finger.
2. Move your fingers, hand, and forearm in a relaxed motion during the shift.

OR

METHOD II
1. Shift up with the finger last used in the old position. This finger becomes the shifting guide finger.
2. Place the new finger immediately upon reaching the new position.
3. Move your fingers, hand, and forearm in a relaxed motion during the shift.

EXERCISE INSTRUCTIONS

1. These exercises should NOT be practiced all at one time. Select and practice a few exercises each day. Especially practice the shifts encountered in your repertoire.

METHOD I

1. G STRING

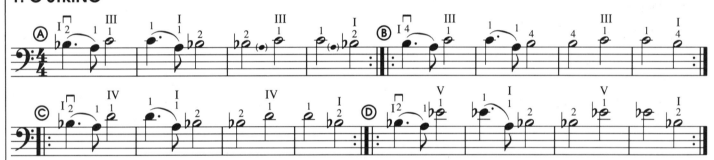

2. D STRING

METHOD II

1. G STRING

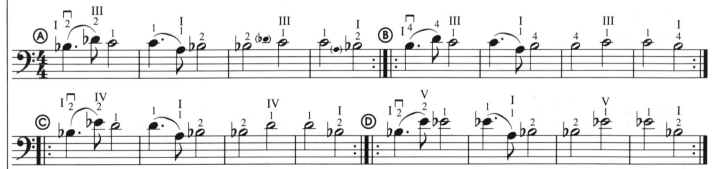

2. D STRING

NEW IDEA

SHIFTING TO A DIFFERENT FINGER – CLASS 3 SHIFT (Ascending)

High Numbered Finger to a Low Numbered Finger
First (I) Position to Third (III), Fourth (IV), and Fifth (V) Positions
Two methods of shifting for the Class 3 shift are presented below in line 116. Your teacher will tell you which method to use.

SHIFTING INSTRUCTIONS

METHOD I
1. Shift with the finger to be used in the new position. This finger becomes the shifting guide finger.
2. Move your fingers, hand, and forearm in a relaxed motion during the shift.

OR

METHOD II
1. Shift up with the finger last used in the old position. This finger becomes the shifting guide finger.
2. Place the new finger immediately upon reaching the new position.
3. Move your fingers, hand, and forearm in a relaxed motion during the shift.

116. SHIFTING TRAINER (All Instruments I to III Pos.)

METHOD I

METHOD II

(Cello only I to IV Pos.)
METHOD I   **METHOD II**

117. SHIFTING ETUDE

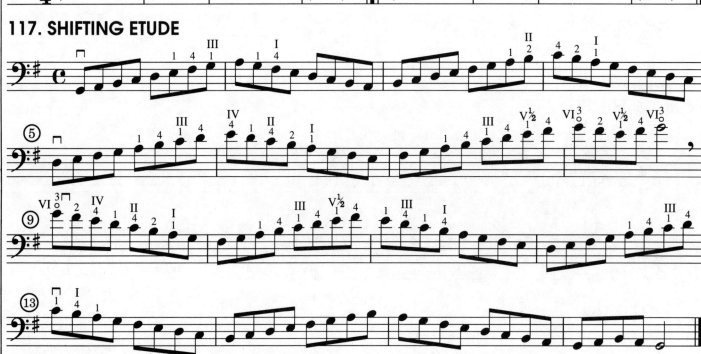

★ Play this exercise with the following bowings:

a. ♪♪♪♪ ♪♪♪♪   b. ♩♪♪♪♪ ♪♪♪♪   c. ♩♪♪♪ ♪♪♪♩   d. ♩♪♪♪♪ ♪♪♪ ♩ ♪

118. BENEATH THY GUIDING HAND

Hatton

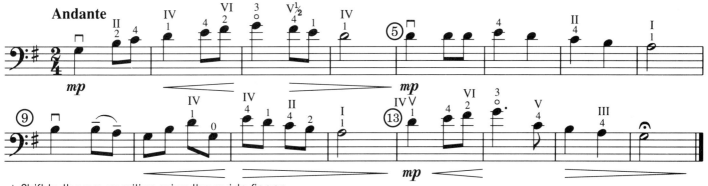

★ Shift to the new position using the guide finger.

119. HOME ON THE RANGE

Cowboy Song

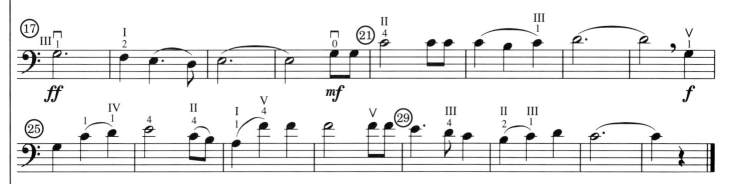

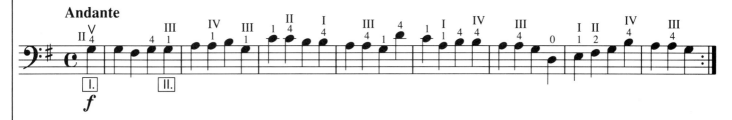

★ Play this piece using vibrato.

120. CANON

Tallis

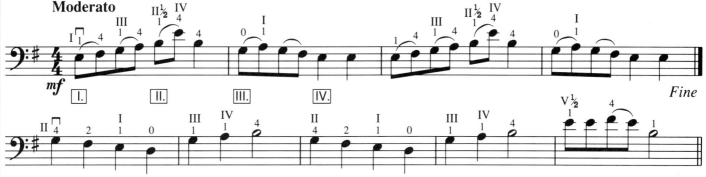

121. SWEET THE EVENING AIR OF MAY

Hungarian-Round

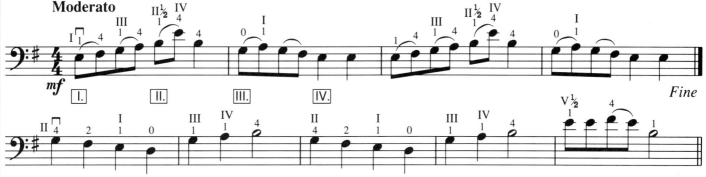

Fine

D. C. al Fine

80SB

SHIFTING FROM AN OPEN STRING TO A NEW POSITION – CLASS 4 SHIFT

NEW IDEA

SHIFTING INSTRUCTIONS

1. Shift to new position while playing the open string.
2. Move your fingers, hand, and forearm in a relaxed motion during the shift.
3. Review the Class 1 Shift if you are unsure of the distance your fingers, hand, and forearm should travel for this shift.

122. SHIFTING TRAINER

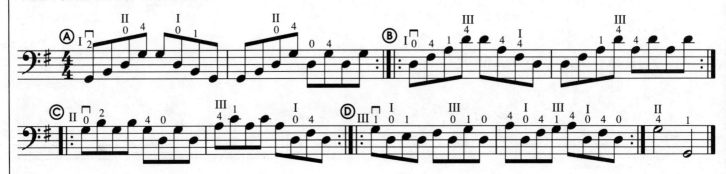

123. SHIFTING ETUDE

Wohlfahrt Op. 45, no. 36

124. FLOW GENTLY, SWEET AFTON

Scottish Folk Song

★ Shift to the new position while playing the open string.

125. SONG OF TRIUMPH

Slovakian Folk Song

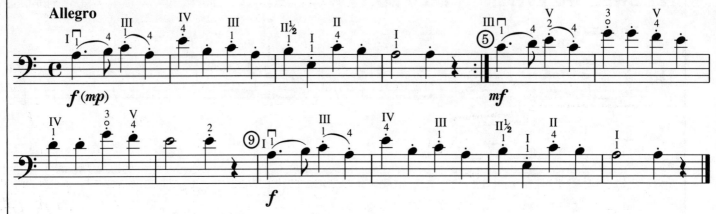

SOLOS

126. MARCH

Bach

Allegro

127. VIOLIN CONCERTO—THEME

Mendelssohn

Andante

128. MINUET IN G—TRIO

Beethoven

Moderato

NEW IDEA

NEW NOTE

HARMONIC

A natural harmonic is produced by touching the string lightly on the note shown. It is marked by a small o above the note.

G String

129. HARMONICS

130. TECHNIC TRAINER

131. SOUTHERN ROSES

Strauss

Vivace

★ Play this piece using vibrato.

132. ALL THROUGH THE NIGHT

Welsh Folk Song

Andante

★ Touch the string lightly with the finger shown to produce a clear harmonic.

133. TECHNIC TRAINER

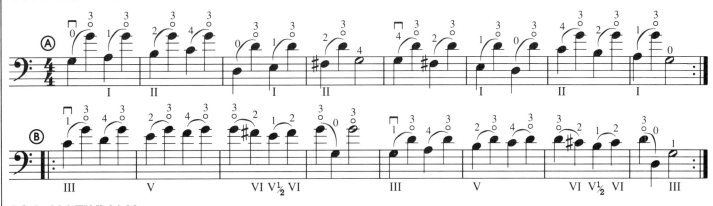

134. HATIKVAH

Hebrew Song

135. TECHNIC TRAINER

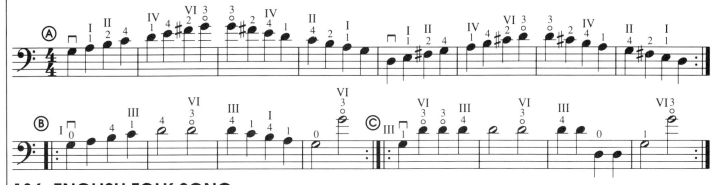

136. ENGLISH FOLK SONG

Traditional

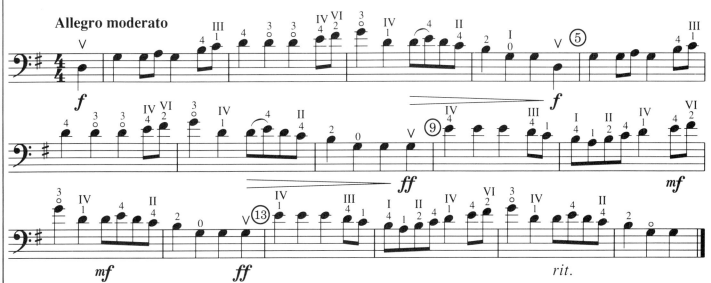

★ What is the musical form of this selection? _____ Circle the notes played with the 3rd finger.

80SB

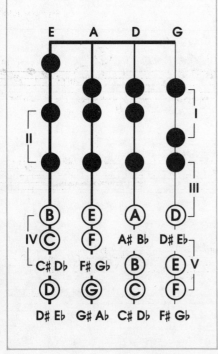

137. SECOND POSITION TRAINER FOR VIOLINS AND VIOLAS

138. F MAJOR SCALE, BROKEN THIRDS AND ARPEGGIOS

THEORY GAME

139. SICILIAN SONG

Traditional

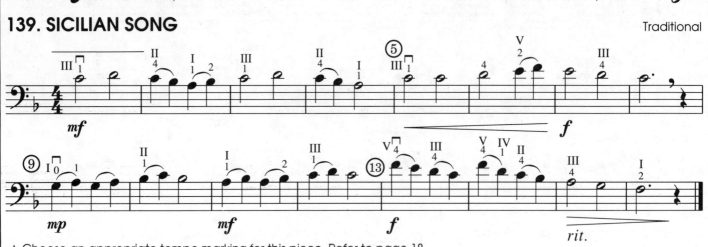

★ Choose an appropriate tempo marking for this piece. Refer to page 18.

140. SIMPLE GIFTS

Shaker Melody

★ Circle the notes where Type III shifts occur.

141. C MAJOR SCALE, BROKEN THIRDS AND ARPEGGIOS

142. ARKANSAS TRAVELER

American Folk Song

★ This is the harmony part. Listen to the melody played by the violins, violas, and cellos.

ETUDES

143. G MAJOR ETUDE

Lee

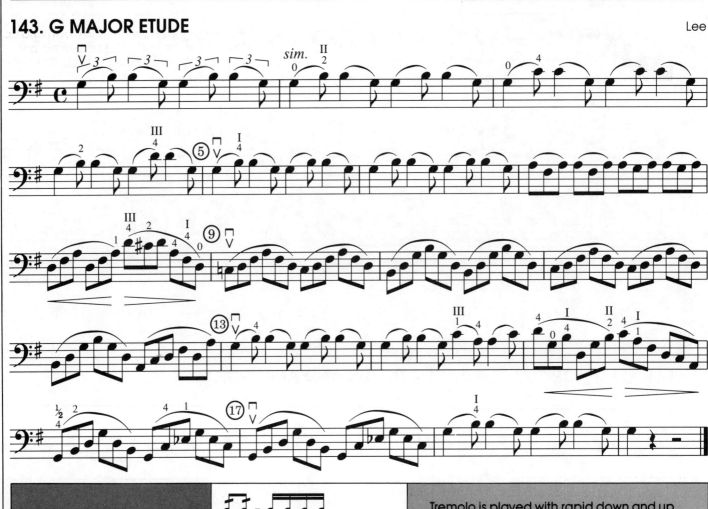

NEW IDEA

TREMOLO

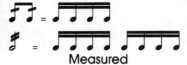
Measured

Tremolo is played with rapid down and up bow movements on one note using an exact number of bow strokes.

144. F MAJOR ETUDE

Werner Op. 12

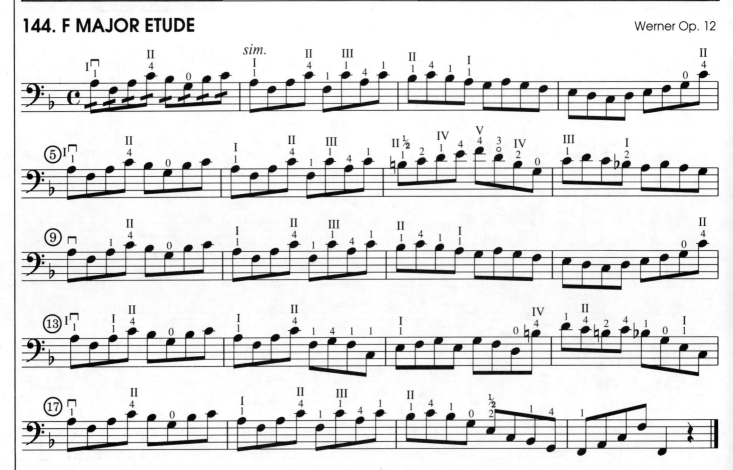

ETUDES

TREMOLO		Tremolo is played with rapid down and up bow movements on one note using an unmeasured number of bow strokes.
	Unmeasured	

145. C MAJOR ETUDE

Dancla Op. 52

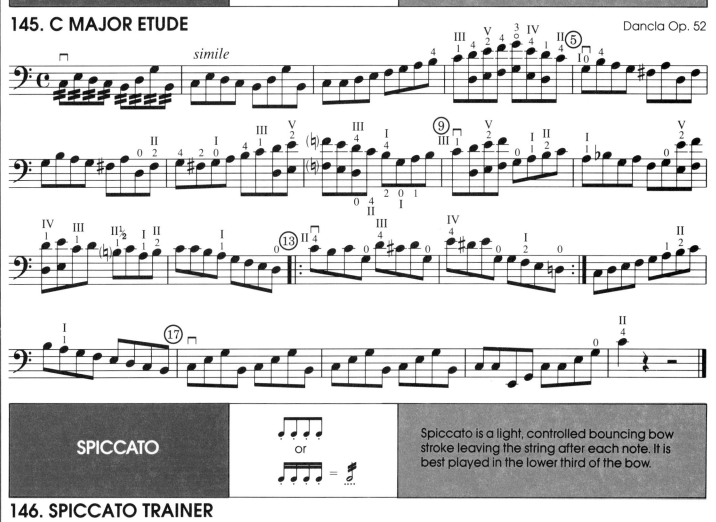

SPICCATO		Spiccato is a light, controlled bouncing bow stroke leaving the string after each note. It is best played in the lower third of the bow.
	or	

146. SPICCATO TRAINER

147. SPICCATO ETUDE

Kayser

MAJOR SCALES

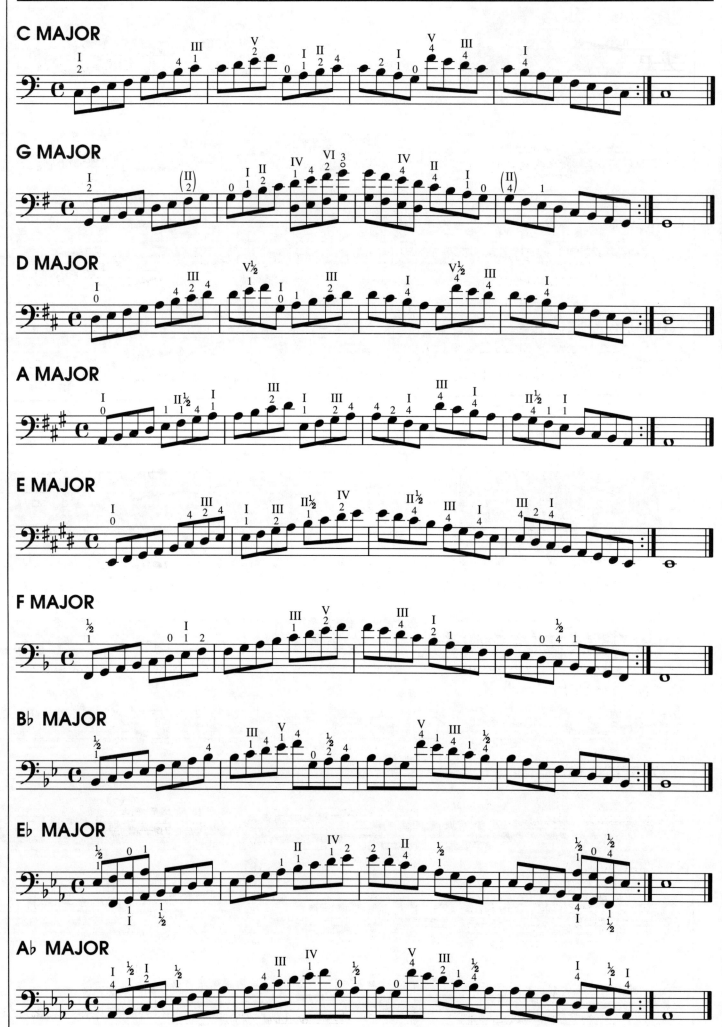

MINOR SCALES (Melodic)

a minor

e minor

b minor

d minor

g minor

c minor

CHROMATIC SCALES

G CHROMATIC

C CHROMATIC

FINGER TWISTERS AND TECHNIC BUILDERS

INSTRUCTIONS

1. Play each measure at least four times with each assigned Rhythm or Bowing Pattern.
2. Start slowly, and upon mastering the exercise(s) gradually increase the tempo.
3. Play each exercise (finger pattern) on all four strings.
4. Listen carefully and think through each finger pattern to help achieve accurate intonation.

1. FIRST (I) POSITION

2. HALF (½) POSITION

3. SECOND (II) POSITION

4. THIRD (III) POSITION

5. FOURTH (IV) POSITION

6. FIFTH (V) POSITION

RHYTHM AND BOWING PATTERNS